My First Book of
WORDS

by Diane Stortz

Illustrated by
Terri Osborne

I
CAN DRESS MYSELF.

t-shirt

belt

shoes

jeans

I
LIKE
TO EAT.

I
LIKE
MY ROOM.

IT'S
TIME
TO PLAY!

ball

train

doll

blocks

teddy bear

toy box

truck

WHAT
IS THE
WEATHER TODAY?

THIS
IS MY
FAMILY.

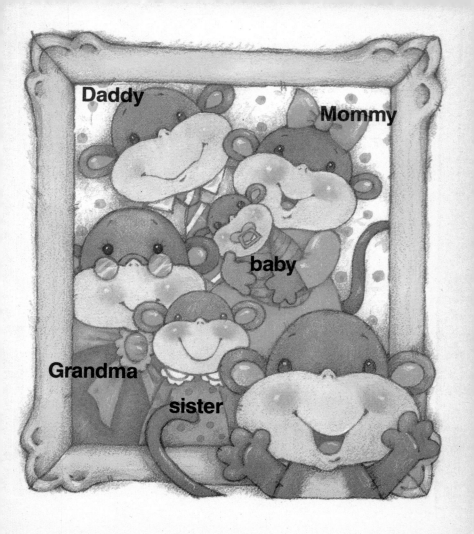

I
GO TO
SCHOOL.

I
LIKE MY
ANIMAL
FRIENDS.

COME TO MY BIRTHDAY PARTY!

balloons

ice cream

presents

hats

candles

cake

I
LIKE TO
RIDE.

train

tricycle

bus

boat

airplane

IT'S TIME
TO SAY
GOOD-NIGHT.

washcloth

bubbles

towel

bathtub

soap